Erik Larsen
creator • writer • artist • inker

Chris Eliopoulos
letterer

Gregory Wright
Steve Oliff
colorists

Jannie Wong
editor

Olyoptics
color separations

**Interior covers, pin ups, backcover and
"Urban Storm" segment colored by Erik Larsen
and separated by Digital Chameleon**

Erik Larsen
Bob Chapman
collection designers

Image Comics
Tony Lobito • publisher
Kyle Zimmerman • promotions
Germaine Zachariah • distribution
Marika Bristol • production manager
Kelly Van Landingham • administrative assistant

Dedication

Chris Vito was my best friend and the best man at my wedding in May of '92. I met Chris in fifth grade and we've been pals ever since. He's encouraged me a lot over the years. I've never known a better drummer, fisherman or friend.

Chris died on February 6th, 1993 around two in the morning. I miss him a lot. I dedicate this book and my whole bloody career to him. Here's to you, Guy, I hope that wherever you are there's good fishing and babes galore!

THE SAVAGE DRAGON is published by Image Comics, 2400 E. Katella Blvd., Suite 1065, Anaheim, CA 92806. DRAGON and THE SAVAGE DRAGON are TM and © 1993 Erik Larsen.

I've drawn comics for as long as I can remember.

Long summer days and weekends throughout my childhood were spent writing and drawing on 8 1/2 x 11 paper, folded in half and stapled up the center. And what a *cast* there was in my unpublished little wonders: **Star, Power House, The Shrew, Zeek, The Deadly Duo, Smasher, Sgt. Marvel, Rock** and dozens more, but my big favorite who held **most** of my attention was **the Dragon**. I drew over fifty comics, some as long as 100 pages, featuring the character.

The Dragon *evolved* as I went along, going from an alien on the mysterious Red Planet, to being the alter ego of **Flash Mercury**. **Flash** changed into **the Dragon** by calling out the name of the wizard **Fon-Ti** (I was a big Captain Marvel fan and I pinched his origin). After that, **the Dragon** went to being the secret identity of **William Jonson** (changing into him in "times of stress" much like a certain green goliath from a major comic book company). Eventually **the Dragon** and **William Jonson** were split from each other to become two separate entities. Each time his situation was changed **the Dragon** was reinvented. **The Dragon** from the Red Planet was an entirely different being than the one that **Flash Mercury** became, **William Jonson's** alter ego was an entirely different entity as well.

Visually, for the first few years he ran around wearing a cape and cowl with his famed fin firmly affixed to his forehead. The first version was a kind a bulky, tattered barbarian-type superhero that lived in the barren hills and swooped down to stop evil doers. The **Flash Mercury** version was leaner, with a **Captain Marvel** cape, black high heeled shoes (this was in the early 1970's), bell-bottomed pants and a needle-like nose. The **William Jonson** version was, again, bulkier with a tattered green cape, a moustache (later on, a beard), high-top sneakers and torn up pants. After **William** and **the Dragon** split, **the Dragon** became pretty much the same as he appears today, the fin became part of his actual head, his skin became green and his feet became two-toed.

In his unpublished history, **the Dragon** was married twice and had three children, most of which were magically transformed into adults to become superheroes themselves. **The Dragon** became part of a huge superhero group called the **Society of Superheroes** (or the **S.O.S.**, as I liked to refer to them), and fought the battle against the forces of evil as their leader.

Shortly after getting out of high school, I stopped drawing comics for myself. **Charlton Comics** had started up a comic called **Charlton Bullseye** which intrigued me. With their regular comics line meeting with plummeting sales, in a bold move they started up **Bullseye** with a rather unique notion...they offered to print comics by whoever was of professional caliber and willing to do the work for *no money* (it should be noted that a few companies have since done the same thing without actually *telling* the creative people involved that they wouldn't be paid). Surprisingly enough, many aspiring professionals leapt at the chance to actually get something in print and Charlton had to tell people to stop sending then stories because they had **too much** material.

I tossed together a **Dragon** story that followed up on the events I'd told in my unpublished comics and mailed copies off to the editor, George Wildman, hoping for the best. I got a polite rejection slip telling me that they simply had too much backlog already and that the book was being cancelled. He encouraged me to send my story elsewhere because he thought the work was "professional enough to do so." Soon after I self published that story along with the work of a couple of friends in a fanzine called **Graphic Fantasy**. **The Dragon** appeared in the first two issues of **Graphic Fantasy**. Review copies were sent out to the Buyer's Guide and everybody else we could think of and soon we were met with rave reviews in all sorts of columns. Cat Yronwode encouraged me to concentrate on my writing career and to use my drawing ability as a way of presenting stories...others liked both the pictures and words.

All reviews responded positively to **the Dragon** which lead to Gary Carlson (a fanzine collector with great aspirations of publishing his own comics), to write me about doing some work for him on a feature for his upcoming black and white superhero anthology book, **Megaton**. I gladly came aboard and **Megaton #1** featured my first professional work in a feature called **Vanguard** which I plotted and drew and Gary dialogued. **Vanguard** was co-created by Gary Carlson and myself, he came up with the name and premise, I came up with the visuals and a name for his robot companion (**Wally**). I ended up doing **Vanguard** stories for the first four issues of **Megaton**. Issue two introduced **Mighty Man** and reintroduced on the final page of the story, **the Dragon**.

The **Dragon** was altered somewhat from his previous appearances in **Graphic Fantasy**. I glossed over much of the unpublished stuff, recreated a character I'd killed off in a previous story and even removed his utility belt, one of the last surviving components left from his original design. **Megaton #3** and **4** featured **the Dragon** extensively, at first fighting **Vanguard** and later helping him fight an enormous crowd of villains.

The **Dragon** appeared for the last time in **Giant-Sized Mini Comics #4** from **Eclipse Comics** in a one page gag story where he yelled at me for not getting him into his own comic book series.

Now, at long last, **the Dragon** has found himself in a title of his own. I started over again with an entirely new beginning rather than continue from the stories in **Megaton** for a number of reasons, making the comic more accessible being the biggest one. **Megaton** had a small but loyal following and an equally small print run and those stories would be for the most part unavailable to the vast majority of the readers.

The thing I liked *least* about the previously published **Dragon** stories was that it seemed as though things had been going on for years. For a potential reader there was no way for them to ever read the back issues that they'd missed because they were unpublished comics sitting in as box in my bedroom closet. Starting over gave me the chance to, for once, have a clean start. That's not to say that the events in **Megaton** and **Graphic Fantasy** will *never* happen, however, they will *probably* never happen.

And so, I reinvented **the Dragon** for the final time. This new character appeared for the first time in **The Savage Dragon mini-series** that is collected here in this volume. While visually quite similar to the previous versions, this new guy has one big difference. This time, he's a police officer. I'm not sure when or why that little inspiration hit but I'm glad it did. It works.

It's been over 20 years since I first drew a character called **the Dragon**. Now, just past the 20th anniversary of his creation and the 10th anniversary of his first published appearance in

Graphic Fantasy. I'm collecting the mini-series that laid the foundation for an ongoing **Savage Dragon** monthly.

I tried something a bit unorthodox when collecting the **Dragon's** adventures in this volume, rather than simply reprinting the stories as they saw print, with flashbacks breaking up the action, I reshuffled the pages putting them into chronological order. Then, I added pages to fill in gaps and expand scenes to make the story flow more as a book rather than a simple straightforward reprint. I hope you like the results.

My biggest personal loss when my house burned down in the big Oakland fire in October, 1991, was all the comics I drew as a kid. The characters and story ideas from my memory of those unpublished comics, will be altered a lot if I reuse them because most of them were pretty silly. Still, they represented a large portion of my childhood and I wish there was some way that I could read through them one more time.

Rob Liefeld asked me if I'd be interested in starting up a new comic book universe with him . It wasn't long before we were joined by Jim Valentino, Todd McFarlane, and later Marc Silvestri, Whilce Portacio and Jim Lee. Together, we formed Image Comics, a company where a bunch of guys do the kind of comics that they want to do without anybody telling them otherwise. To me, *this* is what it's all about. It's about going over to Chris Vito or Aaron Katz's place to draw comics, not intended for publication, just for the *fun* of doing it. It's about staying up 'til three in the morning with Al Harris and Kevin Keyes printing fanzines to bring to a comic book convention the next day. It's about creating the best work you're capable of with your friends and having one hell of a time doing it. I can't think of anything I'd rather do.

I feel like I'm nine years old all over again.

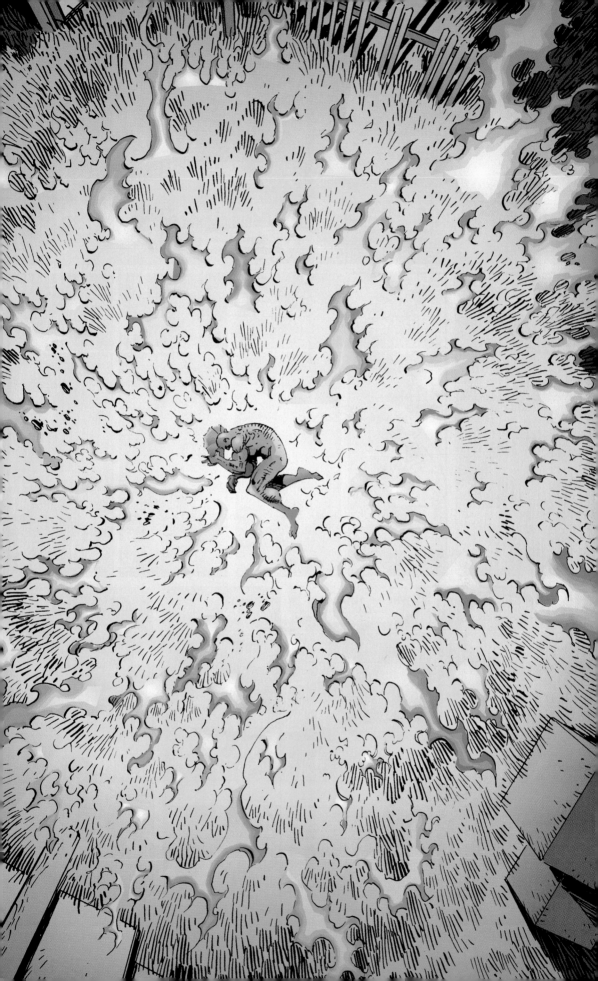

AWAKE?

GOOD.

I'M LIEUTENANT FRANK DARLING FROM THE CHICAGO POLICE DEPARTMENT.

I'VE GOT A FEW *QUESTIONS* FOR YOU.

TO BEGIN WITH... WHO *ARE* YOU?

I...

... I DON'T KNOW.

TERRIFIC.

DO YOU KNOW WHERE YOU CAME FROM?

NO.

CRAKK!

SMAK!

IT'S THE STRANGEST THING I'VE EVER *HEARD* OF.

HE'S GOT *NO MEMORY* OF HIS LIFE PRIOR TO *TODAY.*

YET HE SEEMS TO HAVE FULL KNOWLEDGE OF EVERYTHING ELSE.

HE KNOWS WHAT HAPPENED ON *L.A. LAW* LAST *WEEK* BUT CAN'T TELL ME WHAT HE HAD FOR DINNER LAST *NIGHT.*

HE DOESN'T REMEMBER *ANY* OF HIS FAMILY OR FRIENDS.

IT'S *WEIRD.*

THE DOCS DON'T KNOW IF HE'S A *MUTANT* OR A *SPACE MAN.* PHYSICALLY, HE'S VERY NEARLY HUMAN --

-- EXCEPT FOR HIS *GREEN SKIN* AND THAT *FIN* ON HIS HEAD.

STILL, HE'S AS STRONG AS ALL HELL -- THAT FIRE DIDN'T HURT HIM ...

I DON'T KNOW WHAT TO MAKE OF IT.

LET ME TURN OFF THE T.V.

NO, WAIT!

... *SUPER PATRIOT* IS IN CRITICAL CONDITION.

HE WAS BROUGHT INTO THE HOSPITAL TODAY WITH BOTH ARMS AND LEGS *CRUSHED* BEYOND REPAIR AND HALF OF HIS FACE MISSING.

DOCTORS SAY THAT *IF* HE LIVES, HE'LL *NEVER WALK AGAIN.*

SUPER PATRIOT HAS BEEN FIGHTING CRIME SINCE THE 1940'S WHEN..

OH MY GOD.

UH HUH.

YOU FINISHED?

OH ... UH ... YEAH, SURE.

HMMM ...

HOW ARE YOU *DOING* TODAY, MR. DRAGON?

FINE.

I WANT TO LEAVE.

I UNDERSTAND.

WHERE WILL YOU GO?

I'M NOT SURE.

BUT I CAN'T STAY HERE FOREVER.

WHAT DID YOU JUST CALL ME?

OH! HA... UM... MR. DRAGON.

IT'S 'CAUSE YOU'RE GREEN AND YOU HAVE THAT *FIN* ON YOUR HEAD.

I LIKE IT.

STILL HERE? GOOD.

I'VE GOT A PROPOSITION FOR YOU.

FRANK, WHY DON'T YOU CALL ME *DRAGON* UNTIL I CAN FIGURE OUT WHO I *REALLY* AM.

DRAGON, HUH? CUTE.

LISTEN, I TALKED TO MY COUSIN, FRED. HE COULD USE A GUY WITH A STRONG BACK IF YOU'RE INTERESTED.

HE'S GOT A LOFT OVER HIS WAREHOUSE. YOU COULD STAY *THERE* UNTIL YOU CAN GET BACK ON YOUR FEET.

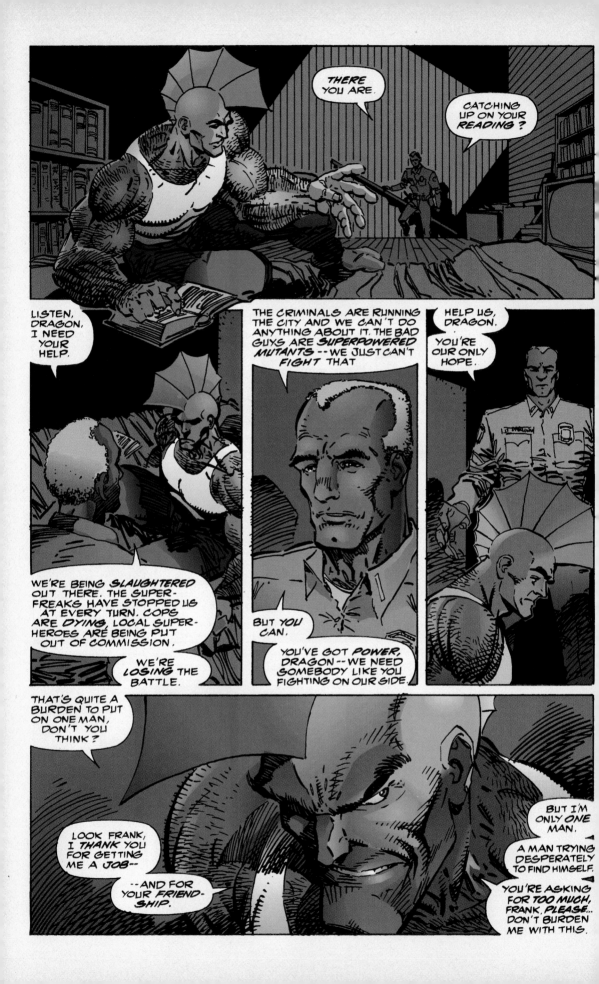

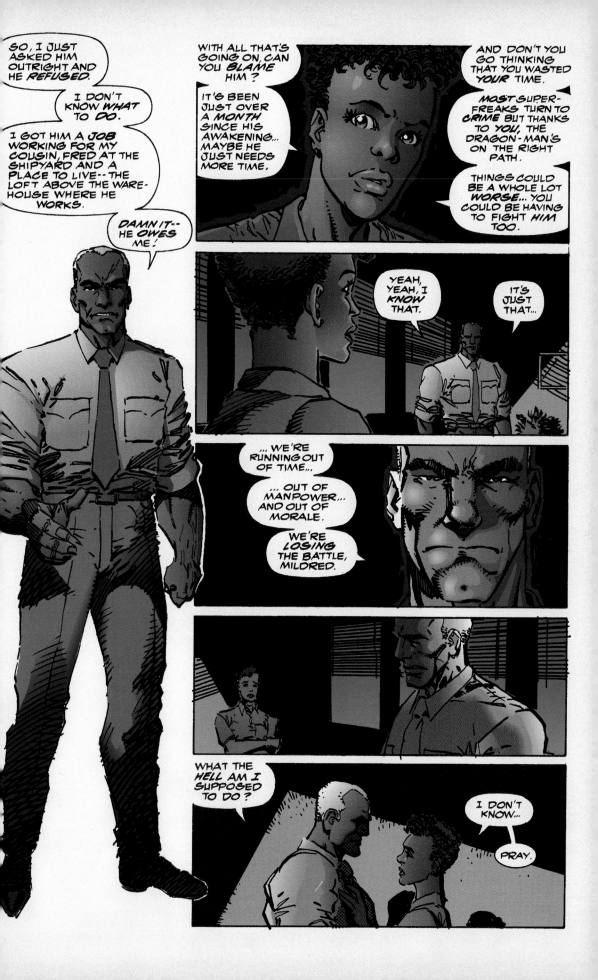

SINCE THE EARLY 1940'S **MIGHTY MAN** HAS FOUGHT A NEVER ENDING BATTLE FOR LIFE, LIBERTY AND THE PURSUIT OF HAPPINESS FOR **ALL** AMERICANS.

TODAY, FOR **MIGHTY MAN,** THAT BATTLE HAS AT LAST **ENDED.**

AT 4:31 PM **ROBERT BERMAN,** THE MAN WHO **BECAME** MIGHTY MAN **DIED.**

JUST A FEW DAYS AFTER HIS SECRET IDENTITY HAD BEEN REPORTED, MR. BERMAN WAS BRUTALLY **BEATEN** AND **STABBED** IN HIS ELGIN, ILLINOIS HOME.

WHAM TV 7

ROBERT BERMAN WAS 67 YEARS OLD. HE REGAINED CONSCIOUSNESS IN THE HOSPITAL ONLY **BRIEFLY** BUT APPARENTLY LACKED THE STRENGTH TO **MAGICALLY TRANSFORM** HIMSELF INTO THE HERO WHO WAS AT ONE TIME DUBBED **"THE WORLD'S MIGHTIEST MAN."**

DAMN.

HE **WILL** BE MISSED.

NOK!
NOK!
NOK!

DRAGON...?

'EVENING, FRANK. LITTLE *TROUBLE* DOWN AT THE OFFICE. BAD GUYS THREATENED *FRED*, I BROKE THEIR FACES AND THEY HAD THE PLACE BLOWN SKY HIGH.

THE *BAD* NEWS IS THAT YOUR COUSIN'S *DEAD*.

GOOD NEWS IS-- I'M READY TO TAKE YOU UP ON YOUR *OFFER*.

OH MY GOD.

ARE... ARE YOU *OKAY*?

PEACHY. I NEED SOME CLOTHES.

HOW SOON CAN I GET STARTED? I'LL NEED TO GO THROUGH THE POLICE ACADEMY.

I'LL...UH... GET YOU SOMETHING TO WEAR.

YOU *SURE* ABOUT THIS?

I'VE GOT NOTHING *ELSE* TO DO.

COUNT ME IN.

BLAM
BLAM
BLAM
BLAM
BLAM
BLAM
KLIK KLIK KLIK

JEE-ZUSS!

NICE SHOOTING! SIX BULLETS-- ONE HOLE.

WHERE DID YOU LEARN TO SHOOT LIKE THAT?

LOOK, I DON'T KNOW.

I DON'T KNOW WHO I AM, HOW I GOT HERE OR WHERE I CAME FROM.

I DON'T KNOW!

I DON'T KNOW!

I'M STRONGER THAN ANY HUMAN'S GOT A RIGHT TO BE AND I DON'T KNOW HOW I GOT THIS WAY.

I JUST DON'T KNOW!

SORRY.

SORRY I SAID ANYTHING.

RELAX, DRAGON.

DON'T LET IT DRIVE YOU CRAZY.

SLASHH!!

A MONSTER...

CORS SENT A DAMN *MONSTER* TO GET ME.

SHAKK!

WHOK!!

CHUNT!!

GLOWBUG...!

LEAVE HIM ALONE, YOU FREAK.

LEAVE MY MAN *ALONE!*

YOU GREEN *BASTARD!*

YOU'RE *MEAT,* FREAK.

BWIDD

BECAUSE I SAY SO.

GOOD ENOUGH.

CLAP CLAP CLAP CLAP CLAP CLAP CLAP CLAP

I'LL KILL YOU... BASTARD.

YOU AIN'T SEEN THE LAST OF ME.

CLAP CLAP CLAP CLAP

GOOD JOB, DRAGON. WELCOME TO THE FORCE.

THANKS.

ROUGH DAY?

I'VE HAD WORSE.

OFFICER DRAGON...

OFFICER DRAGON.

CAN I ASK YOU...

FEW QUESTIONS FOR YOU...

WHY ARE YOU HERE?

WHAT DO YOU HOPE TO ACCOMPLISH?

HOW WAS YOUR FIRST DAY ON THE JOB?

WHAT ARE YOU?

LOOK, I DON'T WANT OR EXPECT ANY KIND OF SPECIAL TREATMENT.

I'M JUST ANOTHER COP. THIS CITY HAS BEEN HELD DOWN FOR TOO LONG. IT'S BEEN TAKEN OVER BY VERMIN WHO PREY ON THE INNOCENTS.

I'M HERE TO TAKE IT BACK.

OF COURSE YOU REALIZE... THIS MEANS WAR.

BOSS...?

DO AS YOU PLEASE, HELLRAZOR.

HIS FEEBLE ATTEMPTS TO RESTORE ORDER ARE OF LITTLE CONCERN TO ME.

HEAR THAT, BOYS?

MORE FUN!

NOW.

HE AWAKENS.

REBORN.

SINCE THE 40'S HE FOUGHT TO PRESERVE THE DREAM AS AMERICA'S FIGHTING FORCE: SUPERPATRIOT. A YEAR AGO HE WAS LEFT A BROKEN MAN, HALF OF HIS FACE MISSING, ARMS AND LEGS SHATTERED BEYOND REPAIR.

SUPER-FREAKS FROM CHICAGO'S VICIOUS CIRCLE DESTROYED HIS BODY AND LEFT HIM TO DIE.

HE'S BACK.

CYBERDATA HAS REBUILT AMERICA'S FIGHTING FORCE AS THE ULTIMATE KILLING MACHINE. IN EXCHANGE FOR REVENGE AND TO BE WHOLE ONCE MORE, HE WOULD HAVE MADE A DEAL WITH THE DEVIL HIMSELF.

THAT'S NOT FAR FROM WHAT HE'S DONE.

NOW, AT LAST, HE'S READY TO DO WHAT HE FEELS HE MUST.

AT LAST.

THE TIME IS NOW.

HI, THERE.

YOU... UH... Y...

I'M... UM... DEBBIE HARRIS FROM DOWN THE HALL AND... UH... DO YOU *LIVE* HERE?

I'M *JUST* MOVING IN.

NOT THAT I'VE GOT TOO MUCH TO MOVE. I LOST WHAT LITTLE I HAD IN... A...

...A FIRE.

UH HUH.

HI.

I WAS STAYING WITH A *FRIEND* FOR A WHILE BUT I THOUGHT IT WAS TIME I GET A PLACE OF MY OWN.

DO YOU LIVE BY YOURSELF?

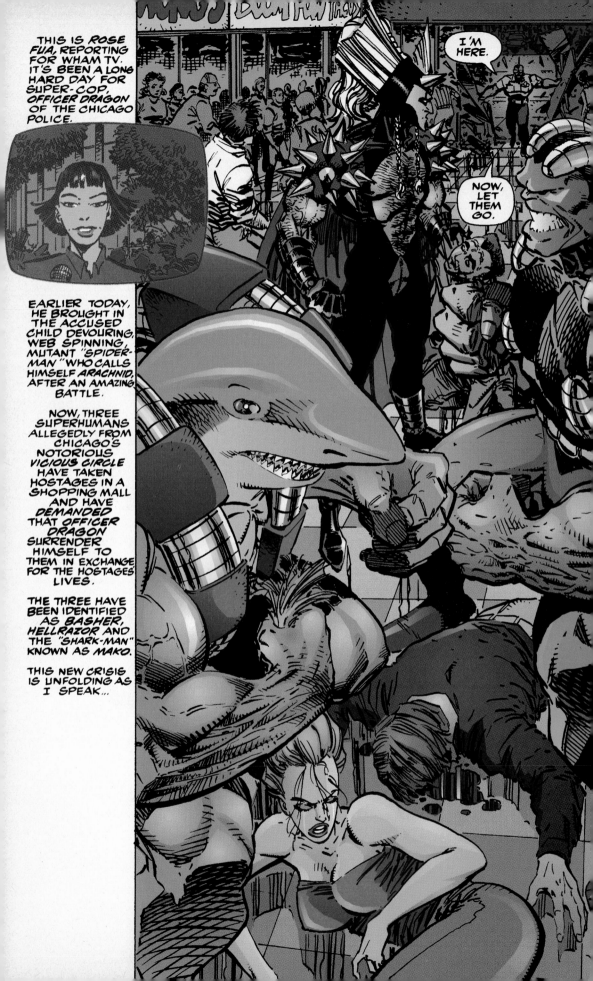

THIS IS *ROSE FUA*, REPORTING FOR *WHAM TV*. IT'S BEEN A LONG HARD DAY FOR SUPER-COP, OFFICER *DRAGON* OF THE CHICAGO POLICE.

EARLIER TODAY, HE BROUGHT IN THE ACCUSED CHILD DEVOURING, WEB SPINNING MUTANT *"SPIDER-MAN"* WHO CALLS HIMSELF *ARACHNID*, AFTER AN AMAZING BATTLE.

NOW, THREE SUPERHUMANS ALLEGEDLY FROM CHICAGO'S NOTORIOUS *VICIOUS CIRCLE* HAVE TAKEN HOSTAGES IN A SHOPPING MALL AND HAVE *DEMANDED* THAT OFFICER *DRAGON* SURRENDER HIMSELF TO THEM IN EXCHANGE FOR THE HOSTAGES LIVES.

THE THREE HAVE BEEN IDENTIFIED AS *BASHER*, *HELLRAZOR* AND THE *"SHARK-MAN"* KNOWN AS *MAKO*.

THIS NEW CRISIS IS UNFOLDING AS I SPEAK...

I'M HERE.

NOW, LET THEM GO.

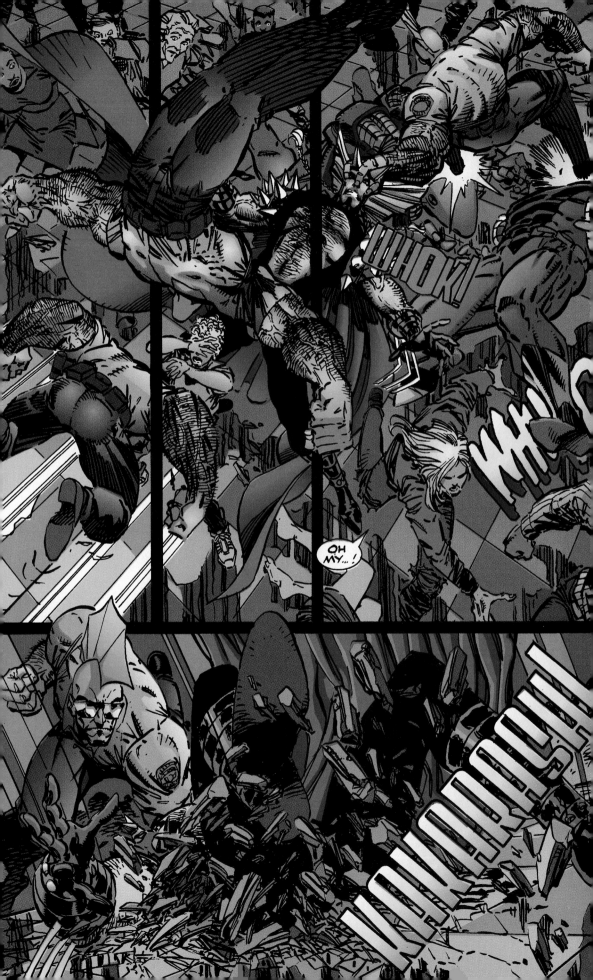

CHOOM!

WELL... I SEE THAT *YOU'RE* UP AND ABOUT.

RUNKK

HE'S ALL *YOURS*, BOYS.

OUCH.

IS THAT GUY ANOTHER ONE OF THOSE *VICIOUS CIRCLE* GOONS?

I HAVE NO IDEA.

HOW LONG HAVE I BEEN OUT OF IT, FRANK?

NINE DAYS.

YOUR BODY SHUT ITSELF DOWN TO MAKE REPAIRS.

MAN, *LOOK* AT YOU.

ALEX, HERE, THOUGHT YOU WERE *DEAD*.

YOU LOST A LOT OF *BLOOD* AFTER *HELLRAZER* CUT YOU OPEN.

BUT YOUR *METABOLISM* IS INCREDIBLE.

THE GASHES ON YOUR *HEAD* HEALED IN A *DAY*.

AND NOW YOU'RE UP AND FIGHTING.

AMAZING.

WHAT *HAPPENED* TO THE *BAD GUYS*?

BASHER HAD A HOLE BLOWN THROUGH HIS *HEAD* THE SIZE OF A *SOFTBALL*.

MAKO AND HELLRAZOR ARE *ALIVE, INCARCERATED* AND IN *INTENSIVE CARE*.

THEY *SHOULD* MAKE IT.

AS FOR *SUPERPATRIOT*...

...HE CRAWLED TO HIS *FEET* AND *TOOK* OFF.

WEIRDEST THING I'VE EVER SEEN.

IT WAS LIKE HE WAS UNDER *REMOTE CONTROL* OR SOMETHING.

I DON'T THINK HE WAS EVEN *CONSCIOUS*.

HAVING YOU OUT OF ACTION REALLY HITS HOME HOW MUCH WE *NEED* YOU.

THE MORE MANIACAL SUPER-FREAKS HAVE TAKEN IT UPON THEMSELVES TO *REALLY* CUT LOOSE.

VIGILANTE DO-GOODERS LIKE THAT "*STAR*" CHARACTER AND US NORMAL COPS...

...WELL, WE JUST DON'T HAVE A *PRAYER* WHEN IT COMES TO DEALING WITH A FREAK THAT HAS ANY *REAL* FIREPOWER.

WE'VE LOST SOME MEN--

IT'S GOOD TO HAVE YOU BACK, DRAGON.

OH, UH...*SKULLFACE*, ONE OF THE FREAKS WHO WHACKED *FRED*, IS FREE. NOT ENOUGH *EVIDENCE* TO CONNECT HIM TO BLOWING UP FRED'S WAREHOUSE.

THE OTHER FREAK, *HARDWARE*, IS STILL BEING HELD, AS HE ACTUALLY *THREATENED* YOU.

WE MANAGED TO HOLD ON TO *HIM* AT LEAST.

I THINK SOMEBODY GOT TO THE *JUDGE*.

THE VICIOUS CIRCLE IS *EVERY-WHERE*.

YOU SCARED THE *HELL* OUT OF ME, YOU BIG JERK.

WHY, MS. WILDE...

... I NEVER KNEW YOU *CARED*.

HAT'S **OKAY,** URSE STEVENS, S. MILLS WAS UST **LEAVING.**

...AS?

Mmmm Hmmm,

I'LL LET YOU KNOW IF I THINK OF ANY WAY YOU CAN **REPAY** ME.

WHAT WAS **THAT** ALL ABOUT?

HOSTAGE NEGOTIATIONS.

WHAT'S ON YOUR **MIND,** SWEETHEART?

YOU **REALLY SCARED** ME.

I'M A **SCARY GUY.**

I MEAN **REALLY.**

I...

...I WAS HERE WHEN **MIGHTY MAN** DIED.

E WAS JUST ISTER BERMAN HEN, OF COURSE, T I **KNEW** HO HE BECAME.

IT JUST ALL SEEMED SO **HOPELESS.**

THOSE EVIL MEN CUT HIM UP AND HE WAS JUST **LYING** THERE, SO **HELPLESS...** I HELD HIS HAND...

...AND HE...

WELL, I DON'T THINK I COULD **STAND** GOING THROUGH THAT AGAIN.

IT ALL CAME **BACK** TO ME THE NIGHT THEY BROUGHT YOU IN...

THERE, THERE.

IT'LL BE OKAY.

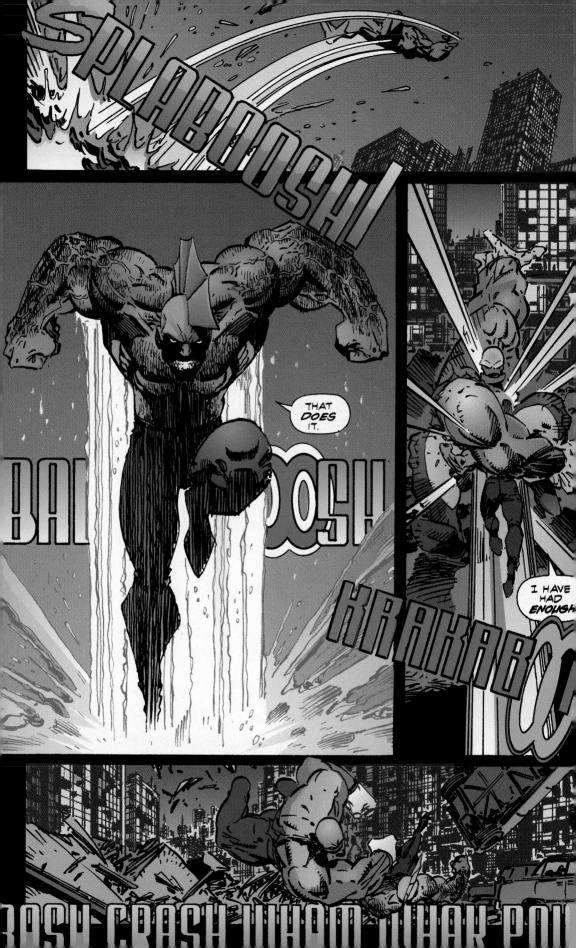

WHY DON'T YOU GO WATCH *TV* OR SOMETHING?

POOP.

I THINK THERE ARE SOME *CARTOONS* ON.

SORRY.

FLICK
FLICK

DING
DONG

GET THAT, WOULD YOU?

BUT WHAT IF IT'S MY *MOM?!*

WE'LL *DEAL* WITH IT.

SHE'S *BOUND* TO FIND OUT SOONER OR LATER.

HELLO?

PIN-UPS

COVERS

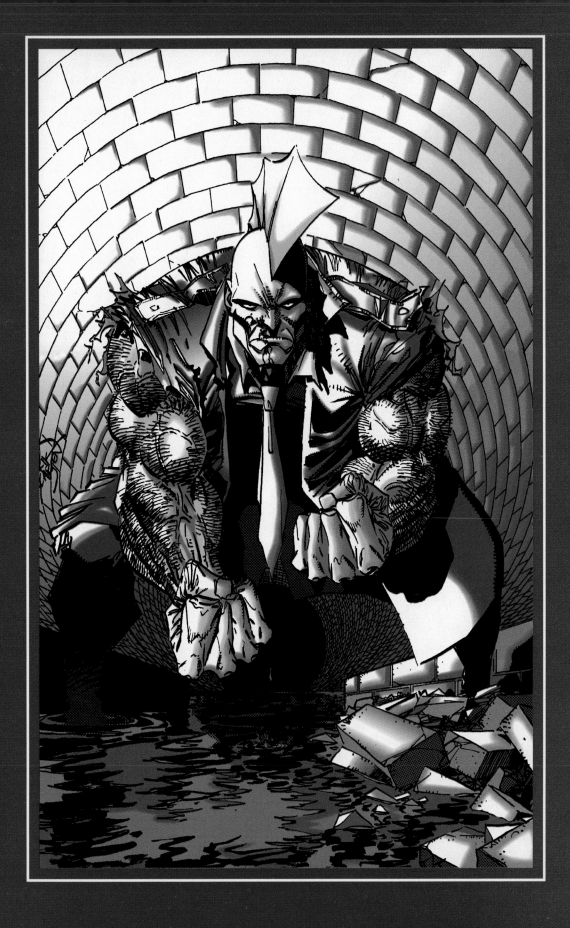

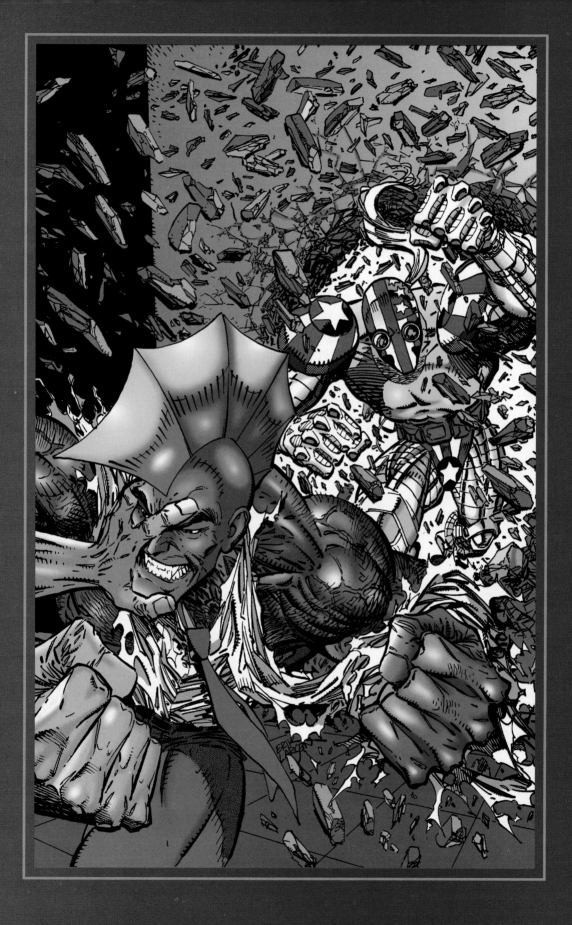

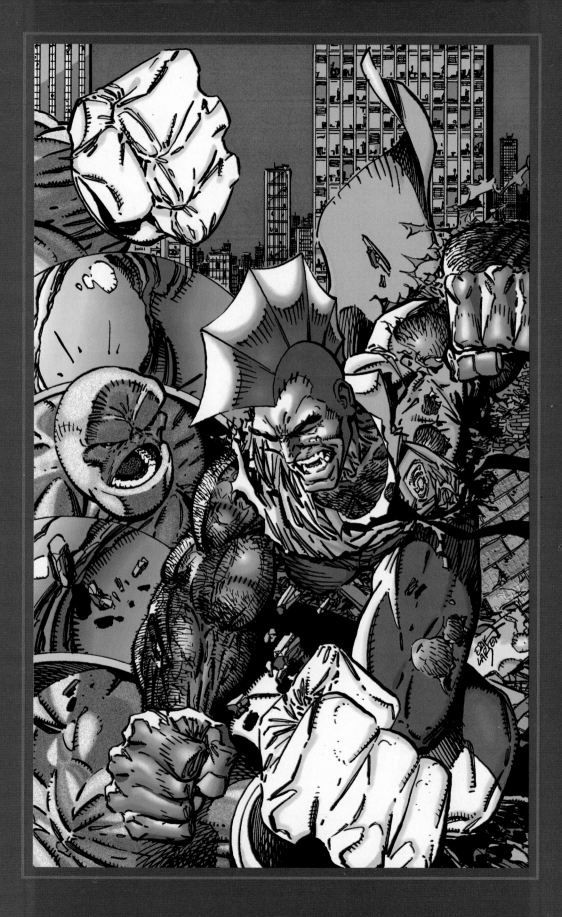

SKETCHBOOK

I've never really been much good at keeping a sketch-book. Must have been something about the pages being already bound in that intimidated me. Most of my unpublished drawings were scrawled on the backs of my comic book original art, on envelopes and on paper bags. It was only after my house and all its contents burned up and I started thinking about doing the Savage Dragon that I started keeping one. It was either that or trying to keep track of all those bloody envelopes and bags!

A lot of what went into this new sketch book were memory sketches of characters from years past and conceptual drawings for the Savage Dragon.

▪ On this page are my memories of how I originally conceived the Dragon. Sort of a cross between Batman, Captain Marvel and Speed Racer. The above drawing also includes some later versions.

■ Dragon, Dart,
Kill-Cat, Rock,
SuperPatriot, Star,
Zeek, etc...

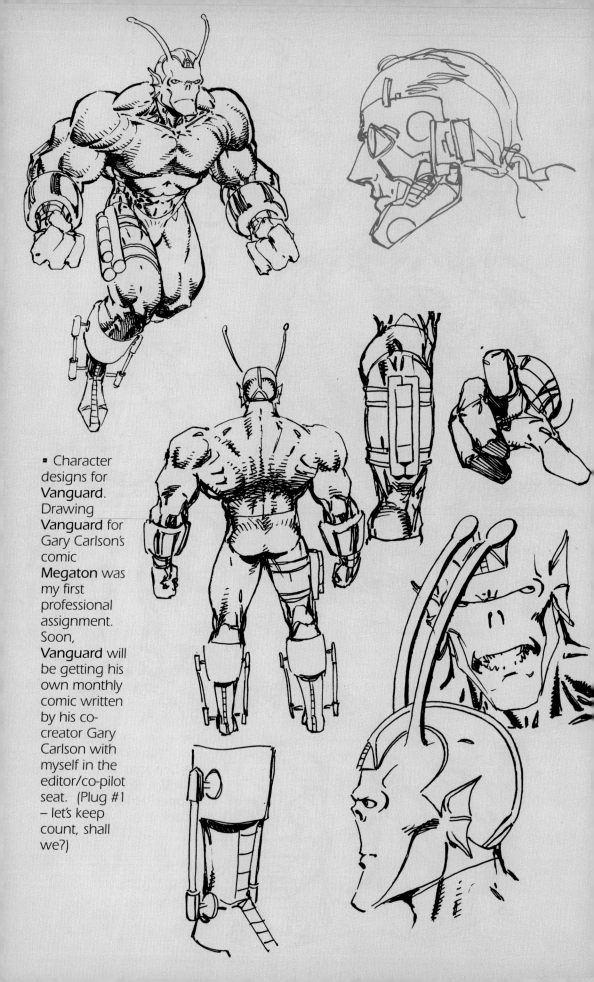

■ Character designs for **Vanguard**. Drawing **Vanguard** for Gary Carlson's comic **Megaton** was my first professional assignment. Soon, **Vanguard** will be getting his own monthly comic written by his co-creator Gary Carlson with myself in the editor/co-pilot seat. (Plug #1 – let's keep count, shall we?)

■ Cover sketches for this book that didn't make it plus an odd assortment of character sketches and doodles.

■ My first drawing of the assembled **Freak Force** team.
I later based an ad on this rough sketch. This team gets formed over the first half
dozen issues or so of the new *Savage Dragon* series.
They get their own monthly book in December 1993. (Plug #2)

■ More random stuff.
The big guy was altered from the waist
down to become Basher from the mini-series
and this book.

EXECUTIONER

MIGHTY MAN

▪ Mighty Man
before...and after!

▪ Sometimes, I can't figure out just what a character should look like – for example: **Overlord**.

I was trying to come up with a major bad guy to take the place of an old foe I created as a kid called **the Bronze Man**.

I went through a lot of names and quite a few costumes before I hit on one I was really happy with.

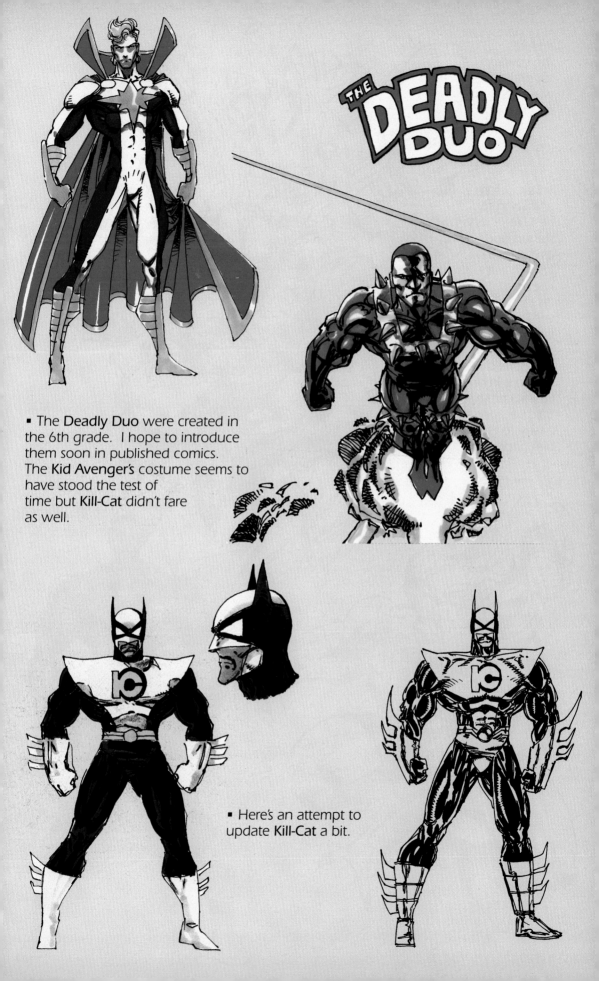

THE DEADLY DUO

▪ The **Deadly Duo** were created in the 6th grade. I hope to introduce them soon in published comics. The **Kid Avenger's** costume seems to have stood the test of time but **Kill-Cat** didn't fare as well.

▪ Here's an attempt to update **Kill-Cat** a bit.

▪ Here's the cover rough that was used on this book.

▪ **Star** before and soon to be. He started out as the bald version but I decided on the hairy version when it came to actually putting him in the mini-series. After seeing it in print, I think I prefer the bald version. I'll find a way to change him back.

MANEATER

GATOR

IRCE W
TAR BUTTS
T TOP
JF
>HOULDER
PAD

STAR
POINTS
TO TOP

R

RED
STRIPE FROM
MIDDLE OF
STAR

R   R

SUPER
PATRIOT

CROTCH HAS
FIVE STRIPES
RED IN THE
MIDDLE

▪ The evolution of **Cutthroat**. These are just a small sampling of the concept drawings for this guy. There were many more.

THE FIEND

• A couple versions of the **Fiend**. I went through a lot of them. Plus, a couple of other characters.

▪ The first drawing of
Rapture and more
unused cover roughs
for this book.

Sometimes I just do
one sketch, other times
a whole bunch. In the
case of this cover, there
were so many different
potential cover scenes
to choose from the
story pages that I had
a tough time settling
on one.

■ More cover roughs and the usual assortment of odds and ends. **Mako** was an old character, given a bit of a new look.

MAKO

■ **Horridus** was another character created years ago. Her name comes from a lizard that looks very much like her. She remained one of my favorites because she's so visually unusual.

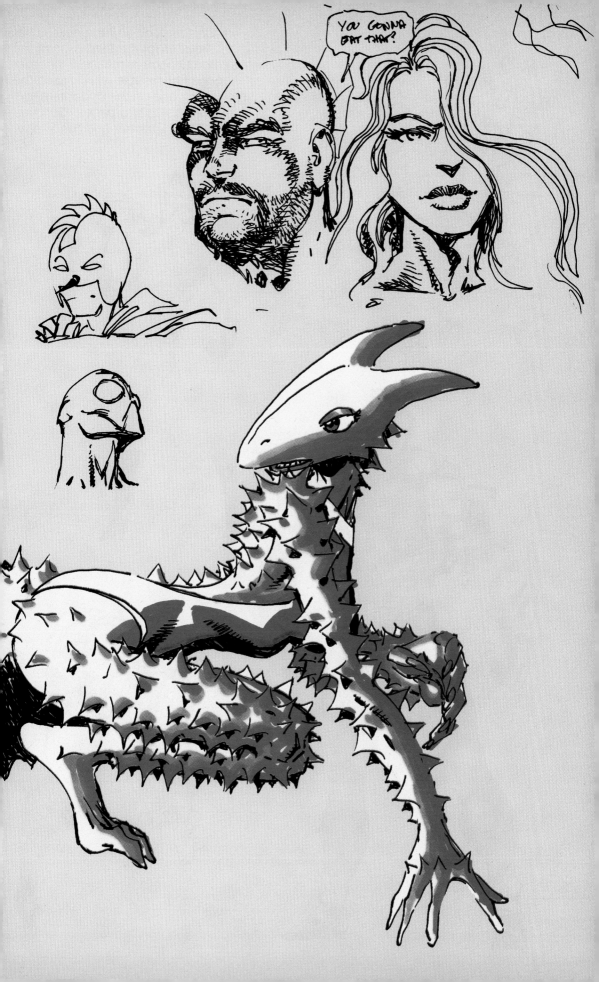

■ On this page and the next, cover sketches for the third issue of the Savage Dragon mini-series – another one I had trouble with. I used the lower left one on the opposite page. Also on these two pages: **Ricochet**, **Dart**, **Smasher** and **the Shrew**.

THE SHREW

40'S

← BLONDE

60'S

ALL AMERICAN SMILE AZA JOHNNY ROMITA + JACK "KING KIRBY

▪ **SuperPatriot** through the ages. Background sketches for the **SuperPatriot** mini-series. (That's plug #3 - ambitious fellow, ain't I?

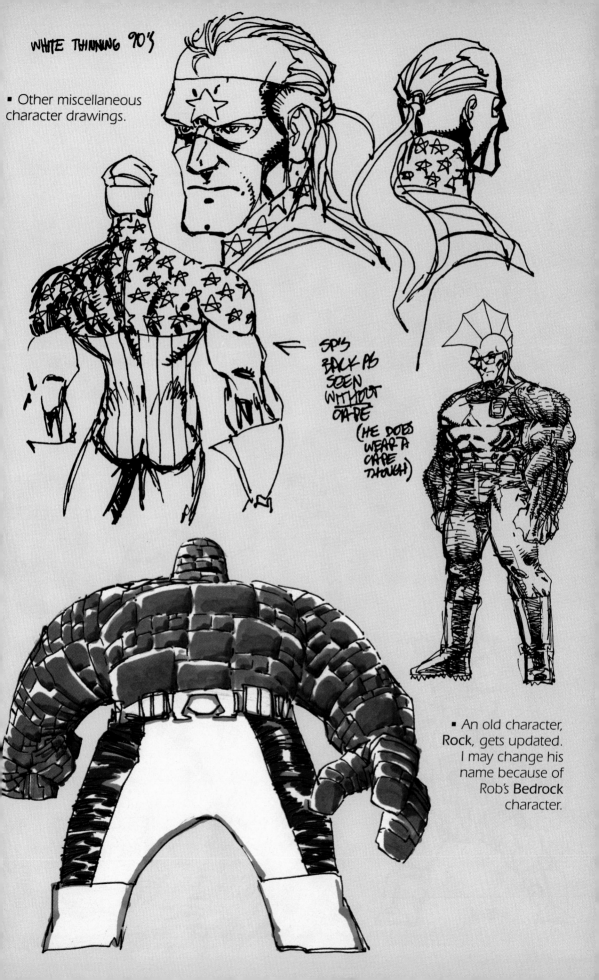

WHITE THINNING 90's

- Other miscellaneous character drawings.

SP'S BACK AS SEEN WITHOUT CAPE (HE DOES WEAR A CAPE THOUGH)

- An old character, Rock, gets updated. I may change his name because of Rob's **Bedrock** character.

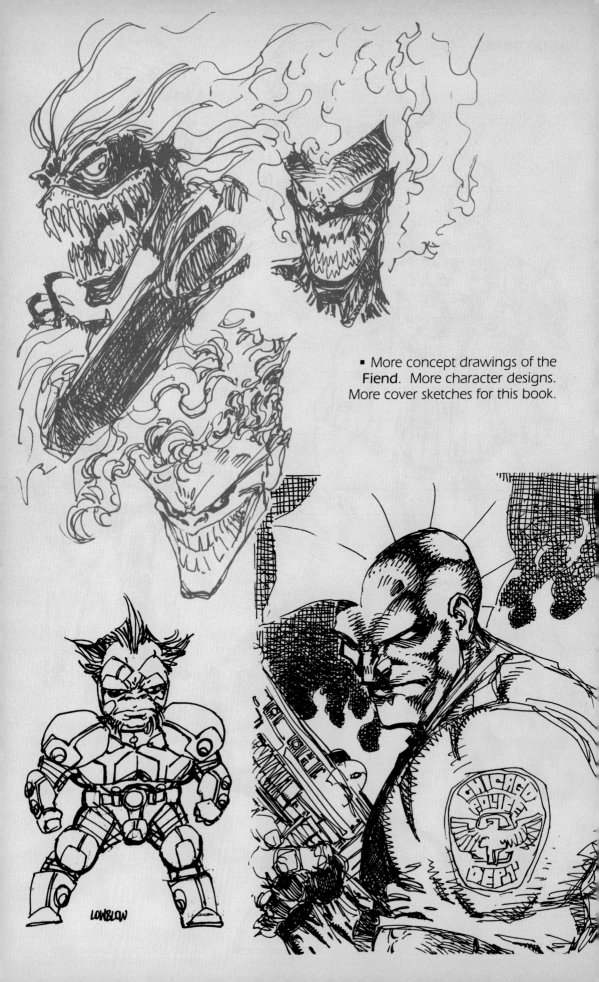

■ More concept drawings of the **Fiend**. More character designs. More cover sketches for this book.

LOWBLOW

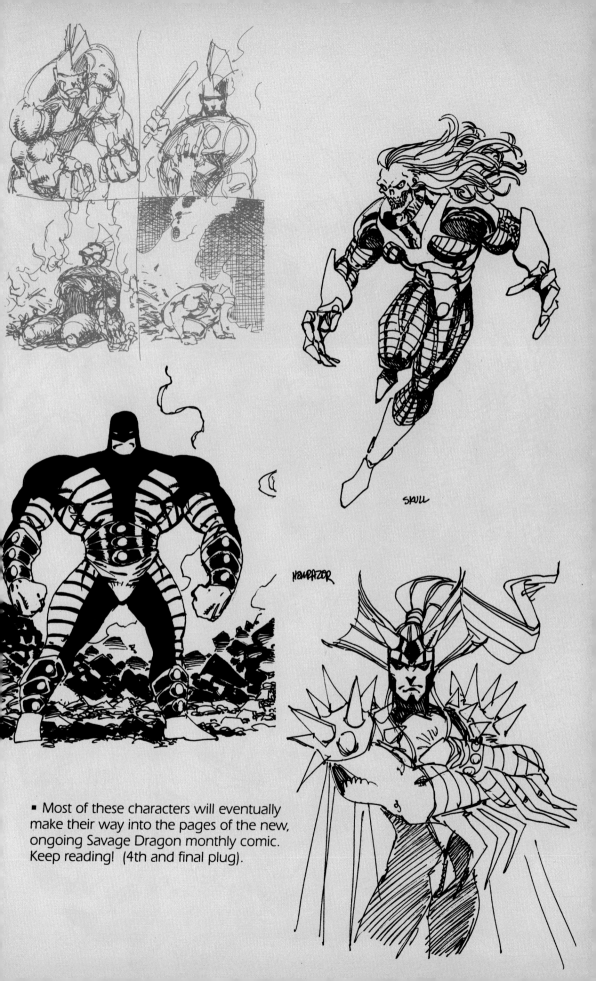

SKULL

NEWRAZOR

■ Most of these characters will eventually make their way into the pages of the new, ongoing Savage Dragon monthly comic. Keep reading! (4th and final plug).